12-26-62

12-26-62

The Golden Stag

AND OTHER FOLK TALES
FROM INDIA

The Golden Stag

AND
OTHER FOLK TALES
FROM INDIA

Selected and retold by

ISABEL WYATT

Illustrated by
ANNE MARIE JAUSS

DAVID McKAY COMPANY, Inc.   •   NEW YORK

THE GOLDEN STAG

MANUFACTURED IN THE UNITED STATES OF AMERICA

VAN REES PRESS · NEW YORK

Typography by Charles M. Todd

Contents

1206903

Contents

These tales the Buddha told
Today still hold
A glint of gold
For you and me.
If we can see . . .

The Golden Stag
AND OTHER FOLK TALES
FROM INDIA

The Golden Stag

AN OLD HUNTER once saw a golden stag. He told no one till he lay on his deathbed. Then he told his son:

"It was up in the hills, far from the king's city. A rill ran over sands of silver. The golden stag led a herd of deer down to the rill, to drink."

This son was a hunter, too. He felt love for all things, and did not wish to kill. It was the wish of his heart to be a hermit and grow wise. But he was born a hunter, the son of a hunter; so a hunter he had to be.

One night, the queen of that land had a dream. In her dream, she saw a golden stag. The golden stag sat on a golden throne, to teach. The things he spoke of were so wise that as she awoke, she cried, "Catch that stag!"

1

Next day, the queen told her dream to the king.

"Did you ever hear of a golden stag in this land, Sire?" she asked.

"No," said the king. "But I will ask my hunters if they have."

Only one hunter had. "My father saw it, Sire," he said. "He told me of it on his deathbed. He saw it up in the hills, far from the city."

"Go and catch it," said the king, "and bring it to the queen."

The hunter went up into the hills, far from the city.

He came to the spot his father had told him of, with a rill than ran over sands of silver.

Footprints of a herd of deer went down to the rill. So the hunter set a snare in the track and hid among the trees.

That night, he saw a herd of deer go down to the rill in the moonlight. The herd was led by a golden stag.

2

The golden stag set his foot in the snare. He cried the cry of capture. At that cry, the herd fled.

Then the hunter saw a thing he had never seen till now. Two of the herd came back to the golden stag. They tried to get his foot free. The thong cut his flesh to the bone; but he was still held fast.

"Go with the rest," cried the golden stag. "Go—you are still free."

"We will not go," said the two stags. "We will stay and die with you."

The hunter felt his flesh creep with pity. He came out from among the trees with his knife in his hand. He stooped down, cut the snare, and set the golden stag free.

"Why did you snare me, hunter?" asked the golden stag.

The hunter told him of the dream the queen had had.

"Then why do you set me free?" asked the golden stag.

"Out of love and pity," said the hunter.

"Hunter, you are no hunter at heart," said the golden stag. "What is the wish of your heart?"

And the hunter told him:

"To be a hermit, and grow wise."

"Brush my back with your hand," said the golden stag.

The hunter did so. Golden hairs from the back of the golden stag clung to the palm of his hand.

3

"Keep them," said the golden stag. "When a man feels love for all things, hairs from the back of a golden stag can make him wise. Now look into my eyes."

The hunter did so.

"What I know, you know," said the golden stag. "Go back now to the queen. What to say to her will come to you."

So the hunter went back to the city. He came to the king and queen and told them how he had met the golden stag and how he had set him free. He told them all that the golden stag had said to him. Then new things came into his mind to say—wise things he did not know he knew.

When he came to an end, the queen cried, "But this is just how the golden stag spoke in my dream! Sire, give this man the wish of his heart. Let him be a hermit!"

"I will," said the king.

So the hunter got his wish and was a hunter no more, but a hermit. He grew so wise that even the king sat at his feet. And all his life he was able to help the king rule his land well, with the help of the golden hairs from the back of the golden stag.

King All-Tusk

1

A HERMIT HAD his hut in a jungle. One day he sat down on a flat rock not far from his hut, to learn a charm by heart.

The name of this charm was "How-to-be-what-I-wish-to-be." It was a charm only for hermits. For it was a charm that did harm if it fell into bad hands. But in the hands of a hermit it did only good; for the wish of all hermits was only to be wise, so as to be of help to man and beast.

Now under that flat rock was a cave. And that day a jackal lay in the cave. He was so near to the hermit that he was able to hear him.

The hermit said the charm out loud again and again,

to get it right. And so the jackal, too, learned it by heart.
At last the hermit got up from the rock.

"I know it by heart now," he said.
"So do I!" said the jackal, out loud. And off he ran.
"Stop, stop!" cried the hermit. "Friend jackal, I beg

you not to say that charm. If you do, you will only do harm."

And the hermit ran, to try to catch the jackal. But the jackal out-ran him and hid away in the jungle. At last the hermit, very sad, went back to his hut. Then the jackal lay down, and put up a paw to scratch his ear, and said:

"Now what shall I wish to be? What do I wish I were? I wish I were the king of all the beasts. Well, then, I will wish to *be* the king of all the beasts!"

So he said the charm; and it was so. Jackals came to him, to bow, as to a king. Wild dogs came to him, to bow, as to a king. Tigers came to him; even the most lordly of all the beasts—elephants and lions—came to him.

So the jackal was made king of all the beasts. And he took the name of King All-Tusk. To show that he was king of even the most lordly of the beasts, he made a lion stand on the back of an elephant; and he, King All-Tusk, sat on the back of the lion. This was his throne.

He grew so proud that one day he said:

"I am king of all the beasts. Why not be the king of men, too?"

So he said the charm again; but this time it was not so. For the charm of "How-to-be-what-I-wish-to-be" made only one wish come true.

But the wish to be king of men, too, grew on him, and grew on him. And at last the jackal said:

"I am king of all the beasts. Well, then, with the

help of all the beasts, I can go and take a city. And in this way I can be a king of men, too."

So King All-Tusk sat on the back of the lion that stood on the back of the elephant; and at the head of all his jackals and all his wild dogs and all his tigers and all his lions and all his elephants, he went to the gate of a city.

All in the city were full of fear when they saw King All-Tusk on his tall lion-seat, and the vast throng of wild beasts he led. They shut the gate of the city in haste, and sent a messenger to tell the king.

The king came to the gate of the city. As soon as King All-Tusk saw him, he called out from his tall lion-seat:

"Give up your city to me, O king. If you do not, I will take it!"

2

THEN THE KING sent a man out of the city by a secret way. He sent him to the hermit in the jungle, to beg him to come and help him. The hermit came back with the man. When he came to the king he said:

"Sire, do not fear. I can save the city from this jackal. But you must let me do it my own way."

"Holy Sir," said the king, "all my men and all my

war elephants are yours, to do as you will with. Only save the city."

"I shall not need them," said the hermit. "All I need is that you shall tell all in the city to do as I shall tell them."

So the king sent his men to beat drums in all the streets and lanes of the city, and to cry the news that it was the king's will that all in the city must do as the hermit told them.

Then the hermit went to the gate of the city. He cried out to the jackal:

"King All-Tusk, how will you take this city?"

And King All-Tusk cried back, from his tall lion-seat:

"I have more than ten thousand lions. I shall make them all roar. That roar will make the walls of the city fall in. That roar will fill all in the city with fear, so that they will have no heart to fight us. In this way shall I take this city."

"Oh!" said the hermit. "So that is how you will take it?" And he went back into the city.

He sent the king's men to beat drums in all the streets and lanes of the city, to bid all in the city make a paste of rice-flour and water. The king's men cried out that it was the hermit's will that each man must stop up his ears with this paste, and the ears of his wife and his child and his cow and his dog, if he had one.

The men of the city did this.

Then the hermit went back to the gate.

"King All-Tusk!" he cried. "How did you tell me you will take this city?"

And King All-Tusk told him again:

"I have more than ten thousand lions. I shall make them all roar. That roar will make the walls of the city fall in. That roar will fill all in the city with fear, so that they will have no heart to fight us. In this way shall I take this city."

"But *will* the lions roar?" said the hermit. "Will the most lordly of the beasts roar when a jackal bids them?"

"You shall see," said King All-Tusk. "I will make this lion that I sit on roar, just to show you."

And he gave the lion he sat on a kick. "Roar, lion!" he cried.

The lion put his mouth down by the ear of the elephant he stood on. And in that ear he gave three long, loud roars.

The elephant shied with fright, so that King All-Tusk fell headlong off his tall lion-seat. He lay in the dust; and the elephant ran amok, and trod him to death.

Then all the wild beasts fled back to the jungle. And each man in the city took the rice-flour paste out of his own ears, and out of the ears of his wife and his child and his cow and his dog, if he had one.

So the city was saved.

And that was the end of King All-Tusk.

Monkey Fat

ᛉᛉᛉ
1

A KING'S SAGE DIED. This came to the ears of a man who was lame and lazy. He said:

"The king will need a new sage to help him to rule the land well. I will put on the dress of a sage, and go to him. If he will take me to be his new sage, I shall be set up for life."

In the old days a sage wore a yellow robe and grew his hair long and did it up in a topknot. So the lazy lame man put on a yellow robe and tied a false topknot on top of his head.

Then he went to the king.

"Sire, you have lost your sage," he said. "Shall I take his place?"

"Wise Sir," said the king, "first stay with me, till I find out how wise you are."

So the false sage went to live in the palace of the king till a time came to test him.

One day, the false sage went out to the king's park to bathe in the lotus pond. In the pond, he took off his false topknot to wash his head.

Now a troop of monkeys lived in the trees in the king's park. One of the monkeys was near the pond when the false sage took off his false topknot, and saw him do it.

The monkey got long grass. He made it into a false topknot. He tied the grass topknot on top of his own head.

Then he began to strut up and down with the lame step of the false sage.

All the rest of the monkeys ran up, to see what he did. They cried out to him:

"Tell *us* this new game. Let *us* play it, too."

Then the first monkey told them:

"I am the lazy lame sage. He must be a false sage, for he has a false topknot. I just saw him take it off, to wash his head."

So all the monkeys got long grass, and made false topknots, and tied them on. They all began to strut up and down with the lame step of the false sage.

When the false sage came out of the lotus pond, he saw the monkeys at this new game. And he saw at once that *he* was the man they had in mind.

"If the king sees this, I am lost," he said. "I must find a way to stop it. The only way is to kill all the monkeys in the park. Now how can I do that?"

And this was in his mind all the way back to the palace.

2

NOW AT DUSK that day, a girl sat in the street to grind rice. At her back was the wall of the palace courtyard.

As it grew dark, she lit a torch to see by and stuck it in the wall at her side.

A stray goat came up, and began to eat the rice as fast as she ground it. She sent him off with a shout and a slap of her hand again and again. But still the goat came back to eat more of her rice.

At last the girl took the torch in her hand, and gave the goat a whack with that. The torch set the hair of the goat on fire. He ran to a hut near by. He began to rub his back on the wall of the hut, to try to put the fire out.

The hut was a grass hut. At once it went up in flame.

The hut was near the king's elephant stables. The wind blew that way. Soon the stables, too, were on fire.

The king's men ran with water. It did not take them long to put the fire out. But the backs of some of the elephants had got burned.

The king sent for his elephant doctors, to heal the burns. But the cure was slow, and the elephants began to run amok with the pain.

Then the king said to the false sage:

"Wise Sir, the time has come when a sage can help me. Can you tell me a swift cure for elephant burns?"

The false sage said in his own mind:

"Now is my time to get rid of the monkeys in the king's park."

To the king he said:

"Sire, I can. Rub them with monkey fat. This cure is both swift and sure."

"But how can I get monkey fat?" said the king. "I shall need so much to heal so many elephants."

"Sire," said the false sage, "your park is full of monkeys. Send your bowmen to kill all that they can find."

"Yes, that will be best," said the king.

So he sent for his bowmen. He told the head bowman:

"Go to my park. Kill all the monkeys you can find. Take the monkey fat to my elephant doctors, for them to rub on the elephants' burns."

The bowmen took bows and shafts and went forth from the city. The path ran along by the wall of the park. At the sound of the bowmen's feet, the king of the monkeys sprang to the top of the wall to see who went by.

When he saw the bowmen halt at the gate of the park, he said to his monkey scouts:

"My dears, I do not like the look of this. What else but us can they kill in the king's park? Go and tell all the rest of our band to flee at once into the jungle. I will stay and find out what it is all about; and when it is safe for you all to come back, I will come and fetch you."

So all the monkeys fled to the jungle. Only the monkey king was left. He hid in a safe lair of his own.

The bowmen went to and fro among the trees with drawn bows, to shoot the monkeys. But they did not find one monkey to shoot in all the park.

At last the head bowman said:

"The king's sage said the park was full of monkeys. They must have all fled. We must go back and tell the king we can get no monkey fat here for his elephants."

And back the bowmen went to the city, to tell the king.

𝓨𝓲𝓨𝓲𝓨

3

"SO THAT IS IT, is it?" said the monkey king. "The false sage knows that we know he is a false sage; so he plots to kill us. I must not let him do that. I must find a way to let the king know his sage is a false sage. Then he will be sure to send him away, and my monkeys will be safe."

So he went to the gate of the king's park, and sprang up, and sat on the archway.

When the bowmen got back to the city, they went to the king. He asked them:

"How much monkey fat did you get for my elephants?"

And the head bowman told him:

"Sire, we got none. We did not find one monkey in all your park."

Then the king said to the false sage:

"How can that be? Did you not say that my park was full of monkeys?"

"I did, Sire. It was," said the false sage.

"Come, Wise Sir," said the king. "Let us go to the park, and look into this odd matter."

So the king went out to his park, and the false sage went with him. He was sure the monkeys had all fled, from the bowmen's news.

"That is just as good as if they were dead," he said in his own mind. "I shall be safe now."

The king went in at the park gate, with the false sage at his side. The monkey king still sat on the arch above them.

As they went under the arch, the monkey king hung

down from it by one hand. With the other hand he was just able to reach the top of the false sage's head.

Whisk! Off came the false topknot.

The false sage put his hands to his head. He gave a start and a cry that made the king turn to look at him.

He saw the false sage with no topknot, and over him the monkey king with the false topknot in his hand.

"Why," cried the king, "you are not a Wise Sir at all!"

"No, Sire," said the false sage.

"Then," said the king, "monkey fat is *not* a cure for elephant burns?"

"No, Sire," said the false sage again.

"I can keep you no longer as my Wise Sir if you are not one," said the king."

"No, Sire," said the false sage yet again.

So the king sent the false sage away. And the monkey king went to the jungle to bring his monkeys back to the king's park.

And from then on, the king made much of the monkeys in his park.

"For," he said, "I did not know a false sage from a true one. But my monkeys did!"

The Three Friends

A DEER HAD his lair near a lake in a wood. In a tree on the bank of this lake, a woodpecker had her nest. In the mud at the edge of the lake, a turtle had his mud bath.

The three were fast friends.

One day, a hunter came that way. He saw the footprints of the deer that went down from the wood to the lake; and in the deer's track he set a trap of strong leather thongs.

At dusk, the deer went down to the lake to drink. He trod on the trap, and the leather thongs held his foot. He cried the cry of capture:

"Friends! Friends! I am fast in a snare!"

The woodpecker flew down from her treetop. The

turtle rose up out of his mud bath. They came to the help of the deer.

"My teeth are sharp," said the turtle. "I can bite the leather thongs."

All night he bit with his sharp teeth at the strong leather thongs. When dawn came, the turtle said, "I have cut Deer free from all the thongs but two. The hunter will soon be here. I need more time."

"I will go and try to keep the hunter back," said the woodpecker.

And off she flew to the hut of the hunter.

Soon she saw the front door open, and out came the hunter, his knife in his hand.

The woodpecker gave a shrill cry, flew at his face, and struck at him with her beak and her wings.

"I must go back," said the hunter. "I shall have bad luck if I go on now."

So he went back into his hut and lay down and slept again.

Then he got up, and took his knife.

"This time I will go out by the back door," he said, "so that I do not meet bad luck again."

So out he went by the back door.

But again the woodpecker gave a shrill cry, flew at his face, and struck at him with her beak and her wings.

"I must go back," said the hunter again. "I shall have bad luck if I go on now."

So again he went back into his hut, and lay down and slept.

This time, when he got up, he took his bow as well as his knife.

"If I meet bad luck this time," he said, "I will stab it or I will shoot it."

When the woodpecker saw the bow and the knife, she flew to her friends.

"The hunter is on his way!" she cried out to them.

The turtle had cut the deer's foot free from all the thongs but one. Blood was on his mouth. He grew weak; but still he bit at the last thong of leather.

The deer saw the hunter stride out of the wood, his knife and his bow in his hand. In his fear, he burst the last thong of the snare and fled into the wood.

The woodpecker flew to her treetop. But the turtle was so weak that he just lay still on the grass.

"I have lost the deer," said the hunter, "but at least I will have the turtle."

And he took him up, thrust him into a bag, and tied the bag up tight.

The deer saw all this. "Now I must do for Turtle what Turtle did for me," he said.

So he let the hunter see him, then took slow steps, as if he were lame and weak. The hunter hung his bag on the woodpecker's tree, and went after the deer, his bow and his knife in his hands.

The deer led him deep into the wood.

Then down flew the woodpecker, to peck a hole in the hunter's bag.

"Turtle, pop out your head!" she cried. "Jump down to the grass!"

The turtle put out his head. "It is too far," he said. "I shall smash my shell to bits."

But as soon as the hunter was deep in the wood, the deer ran back, as swift as the wind. With his long horns he slid the bag down from the tree to the grass; and out crept the turtle by the hole the woodpecker had made.

When the hunter came back, all he saw was his torn bag on the grass. The deer had run, the woodpecker had flown, and the turtle had swum, to the far side of the lake.

Here the deer soon had a new lair, the woodpecker a new nest, and the turtle a new mud bath.

And all three were still fast friends.

The Sneeze
that Won a Wife

1

A KING had a sword tester who took bribes. When a smith made a sword, the sword tester put it to his nose, to sniff at it. If the smith gave him a big bribe, he said the sword was a good one. If the smith gave him no bribe, he did not pass the sword.

One day, a smith made a sword and he gave it to the sword tester, for him to test. But he gave him no bribe. So the sword tester did not pass the sword.

The smith went back to his smithy and soon made a second sword. He slid it into its sheath; and in the sheath he put pepper. Then he took the sword, in its sheath, to the sword tester, for him to test.

The sword tester drew the sword from its sheath, and

put it to his nose, to sniff at it. The pepper on the sword made him sneeze and jerk the sword so that he cut off the end of his nose.

He had a new tip for his nose made out of clay. A dab of paint made it look just like a real nose. But from then on, he did not test swords any more.

Now the king of that land had a son who was in love with the princess of the next land, and she with him. But her father did not wish her to marry this prince, so he kept her shut up in his palace.

The prince tried to find a way to steal the princess from her father. But he did not find one till one day his gaze fell on the nose of the sword tester.

As he did so, a plan came into his head.

He took gold and pepper and a swift steed. And off he rode to the city of the father of his princess.

2

THE PRINCE sat down by the river, by the spot the women of the city went to, to draw water. Soon he saw the old nurse of his princess come along the track, a water jar on her head.

As she bent down to fill the water jar, the prince took out a silver purse and held it out to her.

She took it, and drew the string. She saw that it was full of gold.

"And what am I do do with this?" she asked.

"Nurse, look at me," said the prince. "Do you not know me?"

The old nurse stood still, to stare hard at him.

"Why, you are the prince my princess is in love with!" she cried. "But try as hard as you will, you will not see her. The king keeps her shut up."

"With your help I shall see her," the prince told her. "Tell me, in this land how do you drive out a demon?"

"We take the man to the king's park by night," she said, "and lay him on the stone seat by the gate and say a spell over him; and the spell drives the demon out."

"That is how we do it in *my* land, too," said the prince. "So you must tell the princess to be sick, Nurse, and then tell the king she has a demon."

"That will not help you," said the nurse. "For even if

he sends her to his park, for me to drive the demon out, he will send his men with her."

"I shall hide under the stone slab of the bench," said the prince. "When I sneeze, you must take to your heels. You must get the king's men to do the same."

"Aha, now I see!" said the nurse. "It is a good plan. Yes, I can do it."

And back to the palace she went, with her full water jar on her head.

3

THE OLD NURSE went at once to the princess.

"Princess," she said, "I have seen your prince. He has come to steal you away from the king."

"But how?" cried the princess.

"With a sneeze," said the nurse.

And she told the princess the plan the prince had told her.

"I am sick. Put me to bed, Nurse!" said the princess, full of joy.

The old nurse put her to bed. Then she went to the king.

"Sire," she said, "the princess is sick. I have put her to bed. I fear she has a demon."

"Let me come and see her," said the king.

He came and stood by the bed of the princess. When she saw him come into the room, she began to toss and turn and to rave and to cry out in a speech that she made up as she went along.

"Yes," said the king, "you are right, Nurse. She has a demon. You must take her to my park as soon as it is dark and say a spell to drive the demon out of her."

"But, Sire, is it safe to let the princess go out?" asked the old nurse.

"Safe? Why not?" cried the king. "I shall send my men with you."

Then the old nurse went to the king's men and said to them:

"Take care when we are in the park. The demon will sneeze as he flies out of the princess. Then he will go into the first man he finds. So all keep well out of his way!"

"Trust us to do that," said the men.

As soon as it was dark, the prince hid under the stone bench by the gate of the king's park. He hid his swift steed in the trees near by. But his pepper he took with him.

Soon the king's men came, with the princess and her old nurse in a litter. They laid the princess on the stone bench, and the old nurse stood at her side.

"Stand back," said the nurse to the men, "and take care when you hear the demon sneeze."

She said the spell over the princess; and when she

31

got to the end, the prince took a deep, deep sniff at
his pepper. The sneeze he gave was so loud that all the
king's men shook with fear and fled for dear life.

Then out came the prince from under the bench.

"Quick, to your steed!" cried the nurse. "I shall ride
with you—on the best steed from the king's stable!"

The prince took the princess in front of him on his
steed, and all three rode all night. At dawn they came
to the city of the prince's father and were made man
and wife.

It was hot at the wedding-feast, and the tip of the

sword tester's nose began to melt. He hung his head with shame; but the prince cried out to him:

"Never mind! For some a sneeze brings bad luck, for some it brings good luck. A sneeze lost you your nose-tip; but for me it won my wife. For that I have you to thank; so your sneeze shall bring you good luck yet."

In time, the old king died, and the prince was made king in his place. Then he kept the sword tester about him, and gave him a good place at court.

"Only," said the king, "do not take bribes any more."

And the sword tester did not, but was a wise and just man from then on.

Prince Sun
and Princess Moon

1

A PRINCESS was so lovely that it was said of her:

"When she stands at her window at full moon, it is as if two moons came up."

In this way she got her name of Princess Moon.

When she grew up, the king her father said to her:

"My child, it is time for you to marry. But I fear we shall never find a prince fit to marry my Princess Moon."

"My father," said Princess Moon, "find me a prince keen of eye, quick of mind, strong of arm, wise of heart, and loved by the gods; and I will marry him and love him till I die."

Then the king drew up tests to find out if a man was

keen of eye, quick of mind, strong of arm, wise of heart,
and loved by the gods. And he sent news of the tests
into all the lands in India.

Princes from all lands came to try to pass the tests.
But the princes went again, for not one of them was
able to pass them all.

At last a prince came, and as soon as the princess
saw him from her window, she fell in love with him.
For when he stood, he was like a flame of fire. And
when he sat, he was like an image of fine gold.

His name was Prince Sun.

Then Princess Moon cried out to all her gods:

"Let Prince Sun pass all the tests. For if I do not

marry him, I feel as if I shall die. But if I do marry him, I feel as if I shall live for ever!"

2

THE DAY CAME for Prince Sun's first test. This was to find out if he was keen of eye.

The king led him along a path in his park till they came to two snakes that lay and slept in the sun.

"Are they king snakes or queen snakes?" asked the king.

Prince Sun let his eyes go over them, from top to tail. Then he said, "The one to the right is a king snake. The one to the left is a queen."

"How can you tell?" asked the king.

And Prince Sun told him:

"His tail is thick; hers is thin. His head is round; hers is oval. His eyes are big; hers are small. He is long; she is short."

"You pass the first test, Prince Sun," said the king.

The news ran all round the city. And all the city was glad for the sake of Princess Moon.

3

THE DAY CAME for Prince Sun's second test. This was to find out if he was quick of mind.

The king led Prince Sun out into the courtyard of his palace. He gave him a bag of rice.

"You are to cook me this rice," he said, "in no pot, and with no water. You must burn no wood. You must send the rice to me in a bowl held by two hands, but by no man or woman. I shall stand at my window on an upper floor; the rice must not be sent up any steps to reach me, and it must not come to me along the ground, nor yet by air or by water."

A crowd stood round Prince Sun, to see him try to pass this test. He said to the man next him:

"Bring me a clay bowl, for that is not a pot. And fill it with snow, for that is not water."

He put the rice in the snow in the clay bowl. Then he said, "Bring me straw to burn in place of wood."

He set his rice to cook on his fire of straw. When the rice was soft, he sent for a fresh bowl, and put it into this. Then he said to a child who stood near:

"Take this bowl to the king; you are not yet man or woman."

He put back his head to look up at the king's window, and he saw that the high wall all round the courtyard came to an end by it. So he set the child on the wall; and the child ran along the top of the wall to the king's window; and the king took the bowl of rice.

"You pass the second test, Prince Sun," said the king.

A roar of joy went up from the crowd; and again the news ran like wildfire round the city. And all the city was glad for the sake of Princess Moon.

37

ᚌᚌᚌ
4

THE DAY CAME for Prince Sun's third test. This was to find out if he was wise of heart.

The king's seat was set up in the king's gateway, as it was when he sat to judge any case or to right any wrong. It was his custom then to take off his straw slippers and to share his seat with them.

When he spoke, to judge a case, the slippers beat on each other if he was wrong; if he was right, they lay still.

So now the king put Prince Sun in his seat to judge a case; and he took off his straw slippers, and put them at Prince Sun's side.

The case Prince Sun had to judge was that of two women, each of whom said a baby was hers.

Prince Sun sent for the two women and the baby. He drew a line on the ground, and laid the baby across it.

To one of the women he said:

"Take the child by his hands."

To the other he said:

"Take the child by his feet."

They did as he told them. Then he said:

"Now pull."

Again they did as he told them. The baby gave a little cry of pain; and at once the woman who held his hands let go, and stood and wept. But the other held fast to the child.

Then Prince Sun said:

"She who stands and weeps is the mother."

All eyes were on the slippers at his side. The slippers lay still.

"How did you tell?" asked the king.

Then Prince Sun asked him in turn:

"Who will feel most tender to the child, the mother or not the mother?"

"The mother," said the king.

"Then is she most tender who held fast to the child when it cried out in pain," asked Prince Sun, "or she who let go?"

"She who let go," said the king.

And to the mother he said:

"Mother, take your child."

The mother bent down, and took the child the other woman had put down again. As she held him in her arms, she cried:

"Live long and happy, O King! Live long and happy, Prince Sun!"

And all the crowd took up the cry:

"Live long and happy, Prince Sun! Live long and happy with our Princess Moon!"

5

BUT PRINCE SUN had first to pass a fourth test. He had to show that he was strong of arm.

News was sent with beat of drum into all the streets of the city that in seven days Prince Sun was to wrestle with the best wrestler in all the land. To pass the test, Prince Sun must throw this wrestler, yet he must not put a hand to him.

A ring for the match was set up in front of the king's gate. All the city was in a whirl. Row after row rose the seats; tier above tier above tier.

The prize wrestler came to the match along the Street of the Washermen. As he came, he stole gay robes. Clad in them, he went down into the ring, a garland on his head, earrings in his ears.

He began to strut to and fro, to jump, to shout, to clap his hands at the crowd.

Then Prince Sun came into the ring. He wore only a gold undercloth. In his hands he held a thick elephant strap. As he went past the elephant stables, he had bent down to pick it up.

The crowd sent up a cheer of joy and good will at the sight of him.

"But how *can* he win, if he may not put a hand to our man?" they asked. "It will be sad if our man wins. Prince Sun is just the right prince for our Princess Moon."

Then the match began.

The prize wrestler bore down on Prince Sun like a huge ape, his hands out to take him and grip him fast.

But Prince Sun flung out one end of the strap he held. It went round the wrestler and shot back to the prince. He held both ends in one hand; and with that one hand he took up the wrestler in the loop of the strap, swung him round his head, and flung him to the ground.

The wrestler lay still in the dust. The crowd cried out to him to rise up and go on with the match. But he shook his head with a groan.

So again the crowd cried out, as at the last test:

"Live long and happy, Prince Sun! Live long and happy with our Princess Moon!"

6

BUT PRINCE SUN had still one more test to pass. It was the test to show if he was loved by the gods.

All the city asked, "What test can the king find that will show this?"

When the king told Prince Sun the test, it was this:

"Make me a park in one night, with a lake to match it, and with a palace to match them both."

"But, Sire," cried Prince Sun, "no man can do such a thing!"

"That is true," said the king. "But if the gods love him, and wish him to marry Princess Moon, they will do it for him."

That night, Prince Sun went to his room and lay on his bed to think. He did not feel it right to beg the gods to win this test for him; yet he knew he had not the gift to win the test with no help from them.

Now Sakka, the King of the Sky, sat on his throne of air. And as Prince Sun lay on his bed, with all this in his mind, the air Sakka sat on grew hot.

He bent to look down, to find out why. He saw Prince Sun on his bed. He saw right into his mind.

So Sakka came down from the sky. He came clad as

a sage, in a yellow robe, with his hair done up in a top-knot; he went into Prince Sun's room.

"Prince, what are you thinking of?" he asked.

And Prince Sun told him:

"Wise Sir, the king bids me make him a park, a lake and a palace, all in one night. That is what I am thinking of."

"Then think of it no more, Prince," Sakka said. "If the gods love you and wish you to marry Princess Moon, they will do it for you. Sleep now, my son, and see what the dawn will bring you."

Then Sakka, in his yellow robe and topknot, went from the room. And Prince Sun lay down and slept.

7

AT DAWN, men came into the city in haste, with news for the king.

"Sire," they said, "near our hamlet, a new palace in a new park has grown up in the night."

With joy the king went back with them.

As they drew near, he saw that all round the new park ran a high red wall, with a fine gate under a carved archway.

When he went into the park, he found it green and cool, with all kinds of rare trees and shrubs and plants. Grass and branch were bright with buds; the air was sweet; birds flew from tree to tree, and bees from bloom to bloom.

Then the king came to the lotus lake. Its water was like a gem, clear and full of light. The water was as blue as the sky, yet the light that came from it was as golden as the sun. Rings of lotus grew round its rim, blue and white and rose.

The king went past the lake and came to the palace. It was like a palace in the sky.

Its walls were of clear glass, held up by posts of gold, set thick with gems. Along the clear glass walls hung nets of golden bells. Flags of gold and silver flew from its many bright gables; and golden birds sat on them, and sang sweet songs.

And from the golden gate of the palace Princess Moon came out to meet him, a lotus garland in her hand.

"All is as I see you wish it to be, my child," said her father. "You shall marry your Prince Sun, and this palace shall be your home."

And so it was. And so it still is if they both live.

The Glass House

A MOUSE went to live in an old house. It was such an old house that men did not live in it any more. In the well of this house, the mouse came on a vast store of gold. She cried out three times:

"Who owns this gold?"

"Who owns this gold?"

"Who owns this gold?"

No one said, "I do." So she took it for her own.

Soon after this, a gem-smith came to live nearby. The mouse saw him day by day as she ran to and fro to look for food. He was kind to her; and they grew into fast friends.

One day, she came to him with a gold coin in her mouth.

The gem-smith said, "Who owns gold in this place, Little Mouse, Little Mother?"

"I do, Big Son," said the mouse.

"Why do you bring it to me, Little Mouse, Little Mother?" asked the gem-smith.

"For you to spend on food for us both, Big Son," said the mouse.

So the gem-smith took the gold coin, and he spent it on food for them both.

As soon as the food was at an end, the mouse came again with a gold coin in her mouth and gave it to the gem-smith, to spend on food for them both. And this the gem-smith did.

This went on for some time. Then one day, a cat went by. The cat smelled the mouse. She lay in wait at the top of the well for her.

Soon the mouse came out of the well, with a gold coin in her mouth. *Flap* went the cat's paw and held the mouse down.

"Do not kill me, Cat-Queen," said the mouse.

"Why not, when I need food?" said the cat.

"Do you need food all days, or only this one?" said the mouse.

"All days," said the cat.

"If you eat me," said the mouse, "I shall be only one meal for you. But if you let me go, I will bring you food each day for a year."

"Mind you do, then," said the cat. "If you do not, I shall catch you again. And this time I *shall* eat you."

And the cat let the mouse go.

So now the mouse had to share her food with the cat. This went on for a year. Then the mouse said, "The year is at an end now, Cat-Queen."

But all the cat said was, "You must still bring me food each day. In fact, you must bring me more. If you do not, I shall eat you up."

So the mouse still had to share her food with the cat, and the cat ate more and more of it.

She grew so thin that at last the gem-smith said, "You have shrunk to skin and bone, Little Mouse, Little Mother. Why is that, when we spend so much on food?"

"I will tell you, Big Son," said the mouse. And she told him.

"Why did you not tell me till now?" cried the gem-smith. "But cheer up, Little Mouse, Little Mother. We will soon put an end to this."

He took a block of clear glass, and with his gem-smith's tools he made a hole in it. The hole was just the right size for the mouse to slip into.

"Now just sit still in your glass house, Little Mouse, Little Mother," said the gem-smith. "Be brave when you see your Cat-Queen. She can do you no harm."

So the mouse sat in her glass house. Soon her Cat-Queen came by.

"Give me my food," said the cat.

"Why?" said the mouse. "I have fed you too long as it is."

"Then I shall eat you up now," said the cat.

She sprang at the mouse. But the mouse sat still and safe in her glass house. The sharp glass cut the cat and she died.

Then the mouse went out from her glass house, and ran to tell the gem-smith.

"We will keep your glass house, Little Mouse, Little Mother," he said. "If a cat finds you again, you will be safe if you just pop into it."

Then the mouse ran to the well and came back with a gold coin in her mouth.

"Do you still wish to share, Little Mouse, Little Mother?" said the gem-smith.

"I do and I will," said the mouse. "I gave to the Cat-Queen out of fear. But I share with Big Son out of love."

So the gem-smith spent the gold coin on food for

them both, and the mouse soon grew sleek again. The cats of that place felt such fear of the glass house that no cat tried again to catch the mouse. So she ran free and well-fed and happy all the rest of her days.

The Speech of Beasts

1

LONG, LONG AGO, all men were able to speak with the birds and the beasts. Then, as time went by, the speech of the birds and the beasts grew less and less clear to men.

At last the time came when only wise men knew what the birds and beasts said when they spoke.

The wise men knew a spell that made this speech clear. They were able to pass on this spell to other men, so that to them, also, the speech of birds and beasts grew clear.

But the other men had to be good men, and in need of the help this spell gave them.

One day, a king's sage died. The king was left in need of a new sage to help him rule his land well.

He said to his men:

"Go out and seek for a sage to take the place of my sage who has died."

So the king's men went out into all parts of the land to seek for a sage. One by one they came back to the king. But not one of them had found him a sage.

At last the last one of all came back.

"Sire," he said, "up in the hills I found a hermit who is very wise. So strong is his good will that all the birds and beasts of that part live in peace with each other. He is just the sage you need. But he will not come."

"Then *I* will go to him," said the king, "and beg him to come."

So the king went up to the hills. He found the hermit at the door of his leaf-hut. Birds and beasts were all round him in flocks.

"Wise Sir," said the king, "my sage has died. I need a new sage to help me to rule my land well. I have come to beg you to do this."

But the hermit said:

"Sire, that is a good task for a sage. But my task lies here in the hills."

"What is your task?" asked the king.

"I think good will to all things," said the hermit. "By this means the birds and beasts of this part live in peace with each other. But I see a way to help you. For if the speech of birds and beasts is clear to you, you will in time grow so wise that you will need no sage."

"What must I do for it to grow clear to me?" asked the king.

And the hermit told him:

"I can teach you a spell that will make it so."

"Teach me, Wise Sir," said the king.

"First I must tell you," said the hermit, "that only a wise man may pass on this spell; and then only to a good man; and then only if he is in need of the help this spell will give him. You must pass the spell on to no one. If you do, you will die that same day."

"I will not pass it on, Wise Sir," said the king.

So the hermit told him the spell.

"Say it at the first meal you eat when you get back to your palace," he said.

So the king left the hermit with his flocks of birds and beasts. He went down from the hills to the plain and came again to his own city.

2

WHEN THE KING came back to his palace, he sat down to eat with the queen. As he ate, he shut his eyes, and said the spell in his own mind.

The queen asked:

"Lord, why do you shut your eyes?"

"Lady dear, that is my secret," said the king.

As he spoke, he took a sweatmeat out of the golden sweetmeat dish. He bit into it, and a crumb of it fell to the floor. At once an ant ran to the crumb, and cried out:

"Ants! Ants! The king has upset his honey cart! Come quick, and eat honey!"

At this, the king put his hands on his sides, and shook with mirth.

"My lord, why are you so merry?" asked the queen.

"Lady dear, that is my secret," said the king.

After the meal, the queen went to her bath. When she came back, her skin smelt sweet with the sweet oils her slave girls had spread on it.

A fly said:

"Wife, it is time we went to bed."

"Not yet, my love," said the fly's wife. "The queen has just come from her bath. She smells so sweet, let us stand on her nose and sniff."

And both flies flew to the queen and stood on her nose and began to wave their legs in joy.

At this, the king again put his hands on his hips and shook with mirth.

"My lord, why are you so merry?" asked the queen again.

And again the king told her:

"Lady dear, that is my secret."

"That is the third time you have said that," said the queen. "Tell me this secret, my lord."

And she gave him no peace till he told her what the ant and the flies had said.

"How did you know this, my lord?" she asked then. "How can I be sure you did not make this up, to hide the true secret from me?"

"I did not make it up," said the king. "The hermit in the hills told me a spell that has made the speech of birds and beasts clear to me."

"Tell me that spell!" cried the queen.

"It must not be told," said the king.

"Tell it to me! Tell it to me!" she cried, again and again.

At last the king said, "If I do, I must die."

"Even if you must die, tell it to me!" cried the queen.

And she gave him no peace till at last the king said, worn out:

"Very well, lady dear. I will tell it to you."

3

"WHEN WILL YOU tell it to me?" asked the queen. "Tell it to me now!"

But the king said:

"The hermit told me this spell to help me grow wise. It will be a pity to get no good from it before I die. I will first hear the speech of the beasts a third time and see if it brings me wisdom. Then I will tell you the spell, since you insist that I must.

"Go out and hear it now, dear lord," cried the queen. "It is hard for me to wait to hear it, too."

The king rose, and went out of his palace, to his park. He went to his stone bench, and sat down. This bench stood under a big fig tree.

In this fig tree two monkeys sat and ate figs. One took only ripe figs. The other took them as they came to his hand. He bit them; and if they were still green, he threw them down.

"How silly you are," said the first monkey, "to waste our figs so! The green figs will grow big and ripe if they are left."

"I may be silly," said the second monkey, "but I am not so silly as the king."

"Why so?" asked the first monkey.

"Well, is he not silly," asked the second, "to die at the whim of a wife who cares more for his secret than for his life?"

"Monkey, that is true!" cried the king. "Now I see why the hermit said, *If the speech of birds and beasts is clear to you, you will grow wise.*"

"You grow wise too late, O King," said the second monkey.

"Yes," said the king, "for I have said I will tell her the spell; and so I must."

Then the first monkey said:

"But can you not also tell her that he who is to be told the spell must first have sixty cuts of the whip?"

A third time the king put his hands on his hips, and shook with mirth.

"I can. And I will," he cried.

57

He left the park, and went back to the palace. The queen ran to meet him.

"Did you hear the speech of beasts a third time, dear lord?" she asked.

"I did," said the king.

"And did it bring you wisdom, dear lord?" asked the queen.

"It did," said the king.

"Then tell me the spell now, dear lord," said the queen.

"I must tell you, lady dear," said the king, "that he who is to be told this spell must first have sixty cuts of the whip."

"Let me have them then, dear lord," said the queen. "Do not make me wait to hear this spell."

So the king sent for a slave with a whip.

One, two, three cuts the slave gave the queen. Then the queen cried out:

"Lord, keep your spell, and bid this slave stop!"

The king did so. The queen did not ask for the spell again as long as she lived. And, just as the hermit had said, in time the speech of birds and beasts made the king grow so wise that he had no need of a sage to help him to rule the land well.

The Ugly King

1

THE CHIEF KING in all India had a son. This son was brave and strong and wise, but oh, so ugly!

His name was Prince Kusa.

When Prince Kusa grew up, the king, his father, said to him:

"My son, I shall now give up the land to you, and you shall be king of all the kings of India in my place."

And the queen his mother said to him:

"My son, now that you will soon be a king, we must find a princess for you to marry."

But Prince Kusa said:

"Mother, I am so ugly that no princess will wish to do that. When she sees me, she will run away; and so we shall all be put to shame."

"But if you do not marry and have sons of your own," said the queen, "how can our line of kings go on?"

Then Prince Kusa said:

"Very well, Mother. I will tell you how to find the princess I will marry."

He sent for a goldsmith. He gave him gold. He told him:

"With this gold you are to make me a life-size image of a most lovely lady."

The goldsmith did so.

Then Prince Kusa put a rich robe of silk on the golden image, and set strings of gems round her head and her throat and her arms.

Then he sent the golden image to his mother. "If you can find me a lady like this one," he told her, "I will make her my wife."

The queen had a golden litter made. In this she put the golden image. She sent for her wise men and said:

"Go and find a lady as lovely as this one for my son to marry. If need be, you must seek her in all the lands in India."

The wise men set out. They took the golden image from land to land, all over India. At each royal city they came to, they set up the golden image in her golden litter, and put the litter by the roadside. Then they stood back from it to hear what those who went by had to say.

"Look at that lady! How lovely she is!" they all said. "We have no lady as lovely in *our* city."

When they said this, the wise men went on to the next city, and took the lovely lady with them.

One day they came to a new royal city, and set up the golden lady in her golden litter once again. An old woman with a hump on her back went by. She held a water pot on her head, to fill at the river.

As soon as she saw the golden image, she cried out:

"You bad girl! How dare you slip out alone as soon as I turn my back? If the king hears of this, he will kill me."

She gave the golden image a slap on the cheek. The hard gold hurt her hand. She bent over to look at the

61

image again. Then she cried, "Why, it is *not* you, after all!"

The wise men came to her and asked:

"Who did you think it was?"

And she told them:

"Princess Vati. I am her nurse. This water I have been to the river to fetch is to wash her hair."

So the wise men went to the king of that land. His name was King Madda. They told him:

"Sire, the chief king of all the kings of India sends you this golden image as a gift."

And they gave the golden lady to King Madda. As soon as he saw the golden lady, King Madda cried:

"Wise Sirs, this is an image of my first-born child, Princess Vati! Why does the chief king of all India send such a rich and rare gift to me?"

"Sire," said the wise men, "he sends you her image in her place. For he sends to ask her hand for his son, Prince Kusa, who is now to be our king."

At this news, King Madda was full of joy.

"With all my heart," he said, "I will give her to a prince so wise and good and brave."

2

THE WISE MEN went back with the good news; and the chief king of India and his queen set out to fetch Princess Vati, to take her back and marry her to Prince Kusa.

When they met Princess Vati, the queen said to the king, "She is as lovely as our dear son is ugly. I fear he was right, my dear lord. She will not have time to find out how good and wise and brave he is. She will run away from him as soon as she sees him."

Prince Kusa's father said, "If we can get her to stay with him, she will grow to love him for what he is. So till she has grown to love him, we must not let her see him by day."

"You say well, my dear lord," said the queen.

And she went to King Madda, the father of the princess.

"One thing I must tell you," she said to him. "Prince Kusa will be made king as soon as we go back. Now in our land a new queen must not see the king by day till a child has been born to them. Will this be too hard for the princess?"

"Will this be too hard for you, my child?" King Madda asked Princess Vati.

"No, Father," said the princess.

So King Madda and his queen put Princess Vati in the care of Prince Kusa's father and mother. Her seven sisters, all as lovely as she was, ran to cling to her and kiss her head. Then she sat in a golden litter, and they set out. With her went her old nurse, her slave girls, and a band of King Madda's men.

As soon as they got back to the chief king's palace,

Prince Kusa was made king in his place; and at once he took Princess Vati to be his queen.

But he did not see her by day, nor did she see him.

All the land rang with how lovely to look at the new queen was. It made King Kusa long to see her with his own eyes.

At last he went to the queen-mother.

"Mother," he said, "I *must* see my wife by day."

"Wait till she has a child, my son," said the queen-mother. "Then she will stay with you for ever, and not mind how ugly you are."

"That is too long to wait," said King Kusa. "I must see her *now*. She need not see *me*, as long as I see *her*."

The queen-mother saw that she must let him see his lovely wife. So she said:

"I have a plan. Put on the dress of an elephant trainer, and go and stand in the elephant stable. I will bring her to see the elephants. Then you can see her. But she must not find out who you are."

So King Kusa went to put on the dress of an elephant trainer and to stand in the elephant stable. And the queen-mother went to Queen Vati, and said, "My dear, you have not yet seen the king's elephants. Let us go now and see them."

So the queen-mother took Queen Vati to the elephant stable; and King Kusa was able to gaze his fill at his lovely wife. His stare was so bold and so full of joy that it drew her own eyes to him.

"What an ugly man!" cried Queen Vati. "And his stare is too bold. I shall ask King Kusa to get rid of him."

"My dear, do not do that," said the queen-mother. "He is such a good elephant trainer."

Next day King Kusa went again to the queen-mother.

"How lovely my wife is, Mother!" he cried. "I *must* see her again today!"

"Then put on the dress of a groom," she told him, "and go and stand with the horses. I will bring her to see them. But, my son, do not stare so hard at her this time."

So King Kusa went to put on the dress of a groom, and to stand with the horses in the stable. And the queen-mother went to Queen Vati, and said, "My dear, you have not yet seen the king's horses. Let us go now and see them."

So the queen-mother took Queen Vati to see the king's horses; and again King Kusa was able to gaze his fill at his lovely wife. His stare was so bold and so full of joy that again it drew her own eyes to him.

"What an ugly man!" cried Queen Vati. "And his stare is too bold. I shall ask King Kusa to get rid of him."

"My dear, do not do that," said the queen-mother. "He is such a good groom."

"How like he is," said Queen Vati, "to that ugly, bold elephant trainer we saw in the elephant stable!

"Yes," said the queen-mother. "They are twins."

3

AND NOW IT was Queen Vati who said to the queen-mother, "Do, *do* let me see the king!"

"My dear, you must wait till you have a child," said the queen-mother.

"That is too long to wait," said Queen Vati. "*Do* let me see him *now*. He need not see *me*, as long as I see *him*."

The queen-mother saw that she must let Queen Vati see King Kusa, or think she saw him. So she said:

"I have a plan. On full-moon day we shall hold the Feast of the End of the Rains. On that day the king will make a luck-tour of the city. If you stand at your window and peep out, you will see him as he goes by."

Then she went to King Kusa, and told him, "My son, Queen Vati will not rest till she has seen you. I have told her she can peep at you when you make the luck-tour of the city."

"But she will see how ugly I am!" cried King Kusa.

"Not if you do as I tell you," said the queen-mother. "The oozie who holds the white umbrella over you has the best looks of all your men. Dress him in your royal robes, set him in your seat on your state elephant, and let him act the part of king."

"Good," said King Kusa. "And I will put on *his* dress,

sit in *his* seat, and hold the royal umbrella over him. In
this way I shall see my lovely wife yet once again!"

All this King Kusa did.

As the sun set, the city grew as gay with gems and
flowers as a city of the gods. Rose-red lamps were lit
and hung on all the walls. The streets were full of men;
and women stood at each window, with lotus-buds to
throw to the king as he went by.

With a beat of drums to clear the way, the king's elephant drew near the palace. Queen Vati leaned from
her window. She saw the good looks of the man in the

king's seat; and this made her glad. But he did not look up at her; and this made her sad.

However, the oozie who held the royal umbrella over him *did* look up at her. His stare was so bold and so full of joy that it drew her own eyes to him.

"How ugly that man is!" cried Queen Vati. "And far too bold with his eyes. Can this be the man I saw the other day? Why is he so full of joy when he looks at me?"

And then it came to her:

"Can *he* be King Kusa? Can that be why it gives him such joy to see me? If the king is as ugly as this, that will be why they do not let me see him."

So she said to her old nurse, "Mother Hump-back, when the luck-tour ends, go and see who gets down from the king's elephant first."

The old nurse did as she was told. She came back with the news:

"The ugly oozie got down first."

"Then that ugly oozie was King Kusa!" cried Queen Vati. "I will not stay and be the queen of such an ugly king. Bid my slave girls pack my gems. Bid my father's men bring my litter. I will go back to my father at once. Let all who came with me go back with me."

And this they did.

King Kusa's men went to him with the news that Queen Vati had fled from the palace.

"Sire," they cried, "if we go now, we shall still be in time to bring her back."

But King Kusa said, "No, I will not seek to stop her.

68

For if I do not let her go, she will pine and die. I must give her time to meet this shock. Then I will go and bring her back."

With her, King Kusa's joy went from him. His life was bare with no Queen Vati in it. So at last he went to the queen-mother.

"Mother," he said, "I can get no rest since Vati left me. I must go to her now and beg her to come back. Let my father be king again and care for the land while I am away."

He made three luck-rings round her, and she bent to kiss his head. He put on the dress of a poor man, took his lute, and set out.

4

KING KUSA came to King Madda's city just as the sun set. He went first to bathe in the river. Then he went to the king's elephant stable.

He said to the king's oozies, "If I may rest here, I will play my lute to you."

"Rest, friend," they said.

King Kusa undid the strap of his lute. He sat down and played an air that Queen Vati knew.

As it grew dark, he sang a song. It was one he had

made for her and sung to her in the dark in his own palace. He sang it out loud and clear now for all in the palace of King Madda to hear.

The song came to Queen Vati as she lay in her bed.

"That is King Kusa's song," she said. "Can it be that he has come to fetch me? If so, I will not go."

At dusk after dusk King Kusa sang in King Madda's elephant stable. But all this time he did not see his wife. And all this time she did not send for him.

"It's plain I shall not see her here," he said at last.

So he left the king's elephant stable. He went to the king's potter.

"Shall I make you pots as we make them in my land?" he asked.

"Do so, friend," said King Madda's potter.

King Kusa put a lump of clay on the potter's wheel. He gave it such a spin that it spun till noon. He set the pots to dry and bake; then he set them out for the potter to see.

The potter cried out with joy, "Such pots I never saw! King Madda must see them!"

And he went with them to the king.

Queen Vati's seven sisters ran to look at the pots. As soon as they saw them, they too cried out with joy, "Such pots we never saw! Do let us have them, Father!"

So King Madda gave his potter a bag of gold for the pots, and the potter went away.

Queen Vati's seven sisters sent a slave girl to her room, to ask her to come to them. When she came, they cried, "Look, Vati! Never have such pots been seen in our land! This one must be for you, for it has you and Nurse Hump-back on it."

Then Queen Vati knew who must have made the pot. She flung it down in a rage.

"Keep it!" she cried. "*I* do not want it!"

Day after day King Kusa spent with the king's potter. But all this time he did not see his wife. And all this time she did not send for him.

"It's plain I shall not see her here," he said at last.

So he left the king's potter. He went to the king's fan maker.

"Shall I make you fans as we make them in my land?" he asked.

"Do so, friend," said King Madda's fan maker.

King Kusa made fans, both big and small, of cane and rush, of silk, of gems. Among them he made a palm-leaf fan, and on it was Queen Vati at a feast.

He set them out for the fan maker to see. "Such fans I never saw! King Madda must see them!"

And he went with them to the king.

Queen Vati's seven sisters ran to look at the fans. As soon as they saw them, they too cried out with joy, "Such fans we never saw! Do let us have them, Father!"

So King Madda gave his fan maker a bag of gold for the fans, and the fan maker went away.

Queen Vati's seven sisters sent a slave girl to her room, to ask her to come to them. When she came, they cried, "Look, Vati! Never have such fans been seen in our land! This one must be fore you, for it has you on it, at such a fine feast!"

Then Queen Vati knew who must have made the fan. She flung it down in a rage.

"Keep it!" she cried. "*I* do not want it!"

Day after day King Kusa spent with the king's fan maker. But all this time he did not see his wife. And all this time she did not send for him.

"It's plain I shall not see her here," he said at last.

So he left the king's fan maker. He went to the king's garland maker.

"Shall I make you garlands as we make them in my land?" he asked.

"Do so, friend," said King Madda's garland maker.

King Kusa made garlands, of all sorts of flowers. Among them he made a garland of the five kinds of lotus, and Queen Vati's name was on it in lotus-buds.

He set them out for the garland maker to see.

The garland maker cried out with joy, "Such garlands I never saw! King Madda must see them!"

And he went with them to the king.

Queen Vati's seven sisters ran to look at the garlands. As soon as they saw them, they too cried out with joy, "Such garlands we never saw! Do let us have them, Father!"

So King Madda gave his garland maker a bag of gold for the garlands, and the garland maker went away.

Queen Vati's seven sisters sent a slave girl to her room, to ask her to come to them. When she came, they cried, "Look, Vati! Never have such garlands been seen

73

in our land! This one must be for you, for it has your name on it in lotus-buds."

Then Queen Vati knew who must have made the garlands. She flung it down in a rage.

"Keep it!" she cried. "*I* do not want it!"

Day after day King Kusa spent with the king's garland maker. But all this time he did not see his wife. And all this time she did not send for him.

"It's plain I shall not see her here," he said at last. "I will try again for the last time. If she will not see me this time, I shall be mad to stay. I will go home."

5

SO KING KUSA left the king's garland maker. He went to the king's head cook.

"Shall I cook you food as we cook it in my land?" he asked.

"Do so, friend," said King Madda's head cook.

King Kusa made dish after new dish. He set them out for the head cook to see.

The head cook cried out with joy, "Such dishes I never saw! King Madda must see and taste them!"

And he went with them to the king. King Madda took a bit from dish after dish.

"Who made them?" he asked.

And his head cook told him, "Sire, our new food maker."

"Never have we had such a good food maker," said the king. "Queen Vati's nurse tells me she will not eat. Tell your new food maker to make such dishes for her, and see if they will tempt her. Send him to her with them."

The head cook went back, and told King Kusa this. King Kusa felt his heart swell with his joy.

"At last I am to have my wish!" he cried. "At last I shall see my wife! At last I shall hear her speak!"

Such love, such care, he put into each dish! When all were made, he put them on a food-yoke, and went with them up the steps to the women's part of the palace.

But Queen Vati saw him as he came up the steps.

"He must not stay here," she said. "I must send him away."

She stood in her room, with the door all but shut. As he drew near it, she said, "Go home, Kusa. You will never win me back. I will be cut into seven parts first."

And she shut the door in his face and made it fast with the crossbar.

Then King Kusa said, "What good is all this to me? I must be mad to spend all this time just to get one sharp look and one sharp word from her. I see now that she will never lay her hand in mine in love. So I will do as she bids me. I will go home."

But so deep was his grief that the air that Sakka, King of the Sky, sat on grew hot.

Sakka bent to look down from the sky. He saw Queen Vati, full of rage and scorn. He saw King Kusa, full of grief and love.

"Vati has kept this up too long," said Sakka. "I see it is time for me to take a hand in things."

So he made seven rings, all of them just like King Madda's ring of state. He sent them to the seven kings of seven other lands in India. He sent each ring as if it came from Queen Vati's father. And to each of the seven kings he sent word:

"Queen Vati has put aside King Kusa. Come to me, then, if you wish to marry her. I, her father, will give her to you as your wife."

Then each king was glad and went in haste to King Madda with all his men. All seven kings met near the royal city. Each king asked the rest, "Why are you here?"

And each king told the rest, "King Madda has sent for me, to marry Queen Vati."

Then they all seven cried in rage:

"King Madda mocks us; for how can he give one wife to all seven of us? Let us mock him back. Let us tell him he must do this, or we will take his city."

And they sent a messenger and told King Madda this. King Madda was half out of his mind with fear for his city. He sent for his wise men.

"What am I to do?" he asked them. "Wise Sirs, how can I save my city?"

And the wise men all said, "Sire, you have only one

way to save your city; and that is to send Queen Vati out to them."

"To one? Or to all seven?" cried King Madda. "If I send her to one, the rest will still be our foes. Yet, how can she be sent to all seven?"

"Sire," they said, "Queen Vati's own words will tell you. For she has said, *Never will I go back to King Kusa. I will be cut into seven parts first.*"

6

QUEEN VATI's old nurse came to her room. "Now see what pride and scorn can bring you to!" she cried. "You cast off the chief king in all India, who was wise and good and brave and kind to you. And now your father has only one way to save his city; and that is to cut you into seven parts, and send them to the seven kings."

At this, Queen Vati went white with fear. She rose and ran to the room of the queen, her mother. She wept at her feet.

"Mother! Mother! Tell me my father will not do this to me!"

"Ah, child," said her mother. "You cast off the chief king in all India for so small a thing as his looks; and this is what has come of it. Oh, if only he were here now, to free us from our woes!"

"He *is* here now," said Queen Vati. "He is our head cook's new food maker."

"Child, have you gone mad?" cried her mother.

Queen Vati ran to the window. She opened it wide.

"Look down in the palace yard, Mother," she said. "Do you see that ugly cook who bends over the well to wash his pots and pans? That is King Kusa!"

"Can this be true?" cried her mother.

In haste she went to tell King Madda. In haste King Madda went out to the well in the palace yard.

The new food maker stooped at the well, all soot and grime, clad only in his cook's loincloth. But King Madda stood to fold his hands, and to greet him as king greets king.

Then he sent for Queen Vati. When she came, he said to her:

"Child, beg King Kusa to pardon you for all your pride and scorn."

Queen Vati fell at the food maker's feet.

"O king," she cried, "I kiss your feet. Pardon me. Take me to be your queen again. I vow that for the rest of my life my hand shall lie in yours in love, and I will do your will."

King Kusa bent to lift her up.

"You have my pardon, fair one," he said. "Give me yours for my ugly face. I too vow that my love shall be yours and your will shall be mine for all the rest of my life."

And he felt so strong in his new joy that he began

78

to stride to and fro in the palace yard and to snap his hands and to call:

"Bring me a war elephant! I will go and meet the foes who come to carry off my bride!"

Then King Madda's men put up a tent in the palace yard and went into it with King Kusa to shave him and to bathe him. They put on him a coat of mail, made of gold, with a belt of gems. When he came out from the tent, he was like a prince from the sky.

Then King Madda sent for his war elephant. The elephant came, clad in mail, girt with gold, with gems on his tusks.

King Kusa sat in the king's seat on the elephant's back. An oozie held a white umbrella over him. And out of the city he went by the East gate.

As soon as he saw the hosts of the seven kings, he cried with the roar of a lion:

"I am King Kusa! Let all who seek to live fall down!"

Not one man in all seven hosts did not fall flat on his face.

Then King Kusa sent King Madda's men to bind the seven kings. He led them into the city. He took them to King Madda.

"Sire, here are your foes," said King Kusa. "They are yours to kill or to free."

"They are *yours* to kill or to free, my son," said King Madda. "For you are king over us all."

"Then I free them," said King Kusa. "And since all seven came to seek a bride at your hands, my father, I beg you to give them what they came for. My wife has seven sisters, all as fair as she is. Let them marry these seven kings."

"With all my heart, my son," said King Madda.

So each of the seven kings went back in joy to his own land, each with a lovely queen. And King Kusa went back in joy to *his* own land, with his own lovely queen. In joy the queen-mother went out to meet them and to bring them into the palace. And in joy both kept the vow they had made—to love each other and to do each other's will.

Miss Goat

A HERMIT HAD his hut in the hills. Steps cut in the rock led up to his hut.

A tiger had got too old to hunt his prey. He went to the hermit, to ask for help.

"I can give you no meat," said the hermit, "for I do not eat meat. But if any beast treads on your tail, you may have him to eat."

Just under the hut of the hermit was a cleft in the hills. The track was only two feet wide, with a tall cliff wall on each side. This made it hard for a beast to turn in the cleft, or for two beasts to pass in it. So they did not go much to this cleft.

But one day, when the goatherd went up to the hills for his goats, Miss Goat got left.

"The cleft is a short cut," said Miss Goat. "If I go that way, I shall soon catch up to them."

So she ran into the cleft. She saw too late that the old tiger sat at the far end. He sat with his face to her; so, when *she* saw *him*, *he* saw *her*.

"Oh dear!" said Miss Goat to Miss Goat. "How can I get past him? Yet how can I turn in this cleft?"

So she gave him a smile, and said, "How are you, Uncle?"

"Do not Uncle *me*, Miss Goat," said the old tiger. "Stand still, and let me look at my next meal."

"Oh, Uncle!" cried Miss Goat. "What odd things you do say!"

She did stand still. But it was to think.

Now the hermit had been down to the city, to get salt. As he went up the rock-steps to his hut, he saw Miss Goat stand in the cleft, just below.

He cried down to her, "Why do you stand in the cleft, Miss Goat?"

"To look at Uncle Tiger, Holy Sir," said Miss Goat.

The hermit went up the next step; and then he saw the old tiger, just below. He cried down to him, "Why do you sit in the cleft, Uncle Tiger?"

"To look at Miss Goat, Holy Sir," said the tiger.

"Uncle Tiger says I am his next meal, Holy Sir," said Miss Goat.

"Yes, Holy Sir," said the tiger, "for she trod on my tail."

"Oh, Holy Sir, I did *not!*" cried Miss Goat.

82

"How did you get into the cleft, Uncle Tiger?" asked the hermit.

"From this end, Holy Sir," said the tiger.

"And you, Miss Goat?" asked the hermit.

"From *this* end, Holy Sir," said Miss Goat.

"Face first or tail first, Uncle Tiger?" asked the hermit.

"Why, face first, Holy Sir," said the tiger.

"And you, Miss Goat?" asked the hermit.

"Why, face first, too, Holy Sir," said Miss Goat.

"Where do you keep your tail, Uncle Tiger?" asked the hermit.

"Why, at my back, Holy Sir," said the tiger.

Then the hermit said to the tiger, "But if you met face to face, and your tail is at your back, Uncle Tiger, how did Miss Goat get to it, to tread on it?"

At this, the old tiger got up and slunk off, to sulk in his den.

This left the way free for Miss Goat. Along the cleft she ran, and out of the cleft, and down the hill to catch up with the goatherd and the rest of the goats.

And as Miss Goat ran, she sang this little song:

> "If I face you on the track,
> And you face me as you sit,
> And your tail is at your back,
> How *can* I tread on it?"

The Bold Little Bowman

ᛉᛉᛉ
1

A BOY WAS ONCE born in a market town far from the king's city. He grew up to be the best bowman in all the lands in India. But he was so small that he did not dare go ask the king to take him as one of his bowmen.

"The king will say that such a dwarf can be no good," he said. "He will not test me, or let me show him my skill. Kings think only big men can be bowmen. I will find a big man, and go to him as his page of the bow."

So he went up and down the streets of the town, to look for a big man.

In the Street of the Washermen he saw a washerman, big and tall and strong. He went to him, and said:

"Washerman, tell me your name."

"My name is Big Bima, my boy," said the washerman. "Now you tell me yours."

"My name is Little Bowman," said Little Bowman. "Why is a big man like you just a washerman?"

"It is all I am good for, my boy," said Big Bima. "Now you tell me what *you* are."

"I am the best bowman in all India," said Little Bowman. "But I am too small for the king to take me into his pay. But you are so big that if you tell the king you are a bowman, he will take *you*."

"What then?" asked Big Bima. "I have no skill with the bow."

"No, but *I* have," said Little Bowman. "I will go with

86

you as your page of the bow. When the king gives you a task to do, I will do it, and you will get paid for it. In this way we shall both of us thrive."

"Done," said Big Bima.

So Little Bowman and Big Bima left the market town, and went to the king's city. They stood at the king's gate; and Big Bima said to the porter:

"Go in and tell the king that the best bowman in all India stands at his gate."

The porter went into the palace. He told the king:

"Sire, the best bowman in all India stands at your gate."

"Send him in," said the king.

So the porter sent Big Bima in. Little Bowman went in at his heels.

When the king saw Big Bima he cried:

"This is a fine big bowman! No wonder he is the best bowman in all India! What brings you to me, Big Bowman?"

"Sire," said Big Bima, "the hope that you will take me into your pay."

"I have room for bowmen as big as you," said the king. "I will have a big bow made, the right size for you. And who is this small boy with you?"

"Sire," said Big Bima, "he is my little page of the bow. His name is Little Bowman."

"Then I will take him into my pay, too. We will have a toy bow made for him," said the king in jest.

So now Big Bima was one of the king's bowmen.

2

BIG BIMA had not been one of the king's bowmen long when a man came in haste to the king.

"Sire," he said, "I am from near the jungle. A big tiger lies in wait for men by the road that goes across it. He kills all the men who pass, so that we fear to use that road."

The king sent for Big Bima.

"Now you can show me your skill as a bowman," he said. "Go and kill this tiger."

So Big Bima set off for the jungle, and Little Bowman went with him. Big Bima made great play with his bow; but it was Little Bowman who shot the tiger. Then the men from the near-by hamlet came with great joy and took off the skin of the tiger for Big Bima to take back to the king.

When Big Bima and Little Bowman got back to the city, they went in to the king and Big Bima said:

"Sire, the road across the jungle is safe now. The tiger is dead. Here is his skin."

And he laid the tiger's skin at the feet of the king.

Then the king was glad and he gave Big Bima a big bag of gold.

Not long after this, again a man came in haste to the king.

"Sire," he said, "the men of my hamlet send me to tell you that a big lion feeds on our crops and takes sheep and goats from our herds."

The king sent for Big Bima.

"Go and kill this lion," he said.

So Big Bima set off for the hamlet, and Little Bowman went with him. They hid near the herds, and Big Bima made great play with his bow. But it was Little Bowman who shot the lion.

Then the men from the hamlet came with great joy and took off the skin of the lion for Big Bima to take back to the king.

When Big Bima and Little Bowman got back to the city, they went in to the king; and Big Bima said:

"Sire, the crops and the herds are safe now. The lion is dead. Here is his skin."

And he laid the lion's skin at the feet of the king. Then the king was glad; and he gave Big Bima a second bag of gold.

So it went on. Little Bowman slew wild beast after wild beast; and the king gave Big Bima bag after bag of gold.

At last the king said:

"Big Bima, you are indeed the best bowman in all India. From now on, you shall be my chief bowman."

So now Big Bima was chief bowman to the king.

3

ALL STILL WENT well till the king of the next land came to make war on the city.

Then the king sent for his chief bowman.

"Big Bima," he said, "you are to go out at the head of all my men to fight this king."

Then Big Bima was clad in a coat-of-mail. The king's war elephant was clad in *his* coat-of-mail. And Big Bima was put on the elephant's back, to ride out of the city at the head of all the king's hosts.

Little Bowman, too, put on *his* coat-of-mail. He got up on the elephant, and sat at Big Bima's back.

As the elephant went out at the city gate, Big Bima shook with fear.

"What shall I do, Little Bowman?" he cried. "I do not even know how to hold a bow, much less how to shoot with one."

"Slide down off the elephant's back," said Little Bowman. "*I* will take your place."

So Big Bima slid down off the elephant's back, and Little Bowman took his place.

Then Little Bowman gave a loud war cry and led the king's hosts into the fight. He rode right into the tent of the king.

"Pick up that king by his topknot!" he told his elephant.

The elephant swung up the foe's king by his topknot, and held him safe on his own neck. The king lay still, half-dead with fear; for Little Bowman had set a shaft to his bow, and the king felt its prick at his back.

"Back to the king!" Little Bowman told the elephant.

Tramp, tramp, out of the camp of the foe and in at the city gate went the elephant.

Tramp, tramp, along the city streets and right into the palace went the elephant.

He did not stop till he stood before the king's seat.

"Lay the foe's king at the feet of our king," Little Bowman told the elephant.

And again the elephant's trunk swung up the foe's king by his topknot, and laid him at the feet of the king.

So Little Bowman won the fight, and the next land with it, for his king.

Later, the king sent for Big Bima and Little Bowman. "Why was the best bowman in all India not at the head of my hosts?" he asked.

"Sire, he was," said Big Bima. "Little Bowman is the best bowman in all India."

"But you told my porter that *you* were," said the king.

"No, Sire," said Big Bima. "I told the porter to go in and tell you that the best bowman in all India stood at your gate. Little Bowman stood at your gate as well as I."

"Then if you are not a bowman, Big Bima," said the king, "what are you?"

"Sire, a washerman," said Big Bima.

Then Big Bima and Little Bowman told the king all.

The king found it a huge jest that he had had a washerman as his chief bowman. He was merry with a mighty mirth.

He sent Big Bima back to his own town a rich man; and he made Little Bowman his chief bowman in Big Bima's place. And all India was loud with the fame of the bold Little Bowman.

The King's Friend

1

A KING had need of rare trees to set up as posts in his new palace. So he sent his men out into the jungle, to find such trees for him.

As they came to each one, they put the king's mark on it, and told the tree they must cut it down as soon as the king had come to burn spice in front of it.

The next day the king went to do this. His raft took him up the river to the jungle. As he went from tree to tree, he saw an elephant limp after him. At last, the elephant lay down in the king's path and held up his left hind foot to him.

The king knelt down by the elephant and took the foot in his hand, to look at it. He saw that a long thorn had run into it and made it swell. He pulled out the

thorn, and told his men to warm water for him to bathe
the foot with.

In a day or two the foot was well.

The elephant still went from tree to tree with the
king, to show his thanks. He went to the king's men, to
pull up trees, or to roll logs, or to hold tools in his trunk
for them.

And he went to the men's small sons, to romp with
them in the river. He let them ride on his back, and pull
him by the trunk, and play all sorts of pranks with him.

When the king had been to all the trees that were to
be cut down, his raft came again up the river, to take
him back to the city. The elephant stood on the river
bank, and cast a last look round at the jungle. Then,
of his own free will, he went on to the raft with the king.

When the raft came to the city, the king rode the

elephant in at the city gate; and from all parts of the city men ran to see the elephant who had come with the king of his own free will.

The king rode the elephant to his own elephant stable, and made his mark on his brow with oil. He made him his own state elephant; and they grew to be as dear to each other as a father and a son.

The king had the elephant fed on three-year-old rice from a golden dish. He had the elephant's stall hung with gay red cloths, and its roof set with golden stars. Each day, he had fresh garlands hung on its posts; and each dusk he had a rose-red lamp lit in the stable, to burn all night.

And he gave out with beat of drum that no one was to call the elephant by any name save that of the King's Friend.

2

THEN ONE DAY the king fell sick and died.

Even in the midst of her own grief, the queen did not forget the King's Friend. She was not able to go to him then, for a son had just been born to her. But she sent to the elephant-men, to say:

"The King's Friend will pine with grief if he hears

the king is dead. So keep the news from him till I can come to him."

So they kept the news from the King's Friend.

When the news of the king's death came to the king of the next land, he said:

"That land has no king to fight for it. Now is the time for me to take it for my own."

So he went with a host of his men, to take the city.

The queen had the gate of the city shut, to keep them out. But she had no one to send to fight them at the head of the king's men.

So she said:

"The time has come when the King's Friend must be told."

So she set a fine shawl about her small son, and she bore him out to the stall of the King's Friend.

She laid the child at his feet, and said:

"King's Friend, we have sad news that we did not tell you till now, lest it broke your heart. The king, your friend, is dead. But see the son who has been born to him; and let this son be *your* son, too."

Then the King's Friend put out his trunk to feel the child, and to lift him to his own head. Then he took him down and laid him in the queen's arms.

The queen went on:

"King's Friend, the king of the next land has come to take our city. Will you help your son to keep it? I have no one else to send out at the head of his men."

The King's Friend gave the loud trumpet blare that

he gave when his war mail was put on. The stablemen ran to get his mail and put it on him. After this, they set wide open the gate of the city.

Out went the King's Friend. He gave a loud trumpet call as he ran:

"Ho, all you elephants, ho! A bad king has led you here! Do not help him to take this land from my small son! Run amok! Run amok!"

And all the elephants in the ranks of the foe ran amok, so that all the men who had come to take the city fled in fear.

The King's Friend went back amid the glad cries of the city. And he kept the land safe for the little king till he grew up. And just as the old king had been as dear to him as a father, so the new king grew to be as dear to him as a son.

Monkey-Lord
and Crocodile

MONKEY-LORD had his lair on the bank of a river. In the middle of the river was a small patch of dry land. On it grew the best mango trees in all India.

At dawn each day, Monkey-Lord went to the patch of dry land to eat. He spent the day in the mango patch. At dusk he went back to his lair on the river bank.

From the river bank to the mango patch was too far for him to jump. But a flat rock lay midway. So he sprang from the bank to the rock, and then from the rock to the mango patch.

Now in this river Crocodile had his lair, with Crocodile-Wife. Day after day, Crocodile-Wife saw Monkey-Lord go by.

At last she said, one day, "Oh, how I long to eat Monkey-Lord!"

"So you shall, my sweet," said Crocodile. "I will catch him for you on his way back at dusk."

So Crocodile got up on to the flat rock and lay down on it. His skin was the right rock tint, and he lay so still that it was just as if he were the top of the rock.

When it was time for Monkey-Lord to go back to his lair to sleep, he went to the edge of the mango patch, to spring to the rock.

"The rock looks tall today," he said. "How is that?"

So he stood and cried out:

"Master Rock!"

Crocodile lay still.

Three times Monkey-Lord cried out:

"Master Rock! Master Rock! Master Rock!"

And still Crocodile lay still.

Then Monkey-Lord cried out again:

"Master Rock, why do you not call back to me today?"

"Oho!" said Crocodile. "It seems this rock calls back."

So Crocodile cried back, as if he were Master Rock:

"Yes, Monkey-Lord?"

When Crocodile cried back to him, Monkey-Lord saw his big, long jaws go *yap*. He did not wish to be in them when they went *snap*. Yet he *had* to get past Crocodile, to get to his lair on the river bank.

So now he cried:

"Open your jaws, Master Rock, and catch me as I land."

Now when a crocodile opens his jaws wide, it splits his face so much that his eyes shut into slits.

"Yes, Monkey-Lord!" cried Crocodile.

And he lay on the rock with his big jaws wide open and his eyes shut.

Then Monkey-Lord sprang from the mango patch on to the head of Crocodile. He did not stop, but then sprang in a flash from the head of Crocodile on to the river bank.

"Thank you, Master Rock!" he cried.

And he ran to his lair and crept into his bed and shut his own eyes and slept.

The Lame Cat and the Potter

1

A POOR POTTER made pots out of clay. One day he went out into the wood, to get sticks to make a fire to bake his pots. He saw two wise men go by.

A dead rat lay in the mud. The potter saw the two wise men stand still and look at the rat. One said to the other:

"A poor man who has pity has only to pick up that rat and he will grow rich."

"Yes," said the other, "and he will get a wife who is good and lovely, too."

Then the two wise men went on.

The potter put down his sticks and ran to pick up the dead rat. As he stood with it in his hand, a little lame cat came by, with her tail in the air.

When she saw the dead rat, she said, with a sad little mew:

"Wise-Man Potter, if you will give me that rat, you

will save my life. You can see I am too lame to hunt for my food; and if I do not eat soon, I shall die."

The potter felt such pity for the little lame cat that he held out the rat to her. She took it in her claws, and ate it all up. Then she said:

"And now, Wise-Man Potter, *I* can help *you*."

First, she led him back to his hut, with her tail in the air.

"Bring out all your water pots, Wise-Man Potter," she said.

The potter did as the lame cat told him.

Then she led him to the river, with her tail in the air.

"Fill your water pots with this ice-cold water, Wise-Man Potter," she said.

The potter did as the lame cat told him.

Then she led him back into the wood, with her tail in the air. But she led him to a part of the wood that was new to him. She led him to a cliff that was hung with the wax nests of bees. The air all about it was sweet with the smell of honey.

"Add some of this honey to your ice-cold water, Wise-Man Potter," the lame cat said.

The potter did as the lame cat told him.

Then she led him to a vast grass-patch, with her tail in the air. In the grass-patch were ranks and ranks of men; they all swung hooks, to cut down the grass to dry in the hot sun.

"Let the men drink from your water pots, Wise-Man Potter," the lame cat said.

The potter did as the lame cat told him. The men were glad to stop, and to stand up, and to rest for a little, and to drink deep of the cold, sweet water.

"But we have no money," they told the potter. "So how can we pay you?"

The little lame cat stood by, with her tail in the air.

"Ask them each to put a sack of grass by the wall of your hut when they go home at dusk," she said.

103

The potter did as the lame cat told him. And at dusk each of the men, as he went home, left a sack of his grass by the wall of the potter's hut.

2

AT DAWN, the little lame cat again led the potter to the river, with her tail in the air. He saw a ship slide up the river and glide to rest by the river bank. He saw it was one of the king's ships.

As the men tied the ship fast, he asked them:

"What do you bring for the king this time?"

"Brood mares for his stable," they told him.

They let down the gangway, and led the mares to land. Then they said to the potter:

"We have run out of grass for the mares. Can you tell us who will sell us some?"

"I will," said the potter. "Come with me."

And the little lame cat led them back to his hut, with her tail in the air.

The potter sold all his sacks of grass to the king's men for the king's mares. For his sacks of grass they gave him a sack of gold.

Then the potter said to the little lame cat:

"I got all this gold for that dead rat, Lame Cat.

Thank you. But now I must find the two wise men who told me about the rat, and thank them, too."

"I will take you to them, Wise-Man Potter," said the little lame cat.

And off she set, with her tail in the air.

She led him to the city, and in at the city gate, and along the city streets, with her tail in the air.

She led him at last to the two wise men, and he told them both his tale, and he gave them both his thanks.

"What shall I do with all this gold, Wise Sirs?" he asked them.

"Give it to me," said one. "I will put it into a ship for you; when your cargo is sold in some far land, your

gold will grow into more, and with that you can get a new cargo, that will make it grow still more."

"And I," said the other wise man, "will make you my son-in-law. I shall be glad to have a son who has so much sense and at the same time so much pity."

So the poor potter grew rich, and had a wife as good as she was lovely, just as the two wise men had said when they had first seen the dead rat in the mud. The little lame cat with her tail in the air went to live with them. And all three of them lived happy ever after.

The Jackal Told Me

A HERD OF COWS were put out to grass near the jungle. One of the cows went off into the jungle and got lost. She had her calf in the jungle. A lion-cub was born nearby at the same time. The calf and the cub made friends.

The calf grew up into a bull. The cub grew up into a lion. They were still fast friends.

The lion and the bull slept in the same cave. A hunter saw them go in and out of it.

One day, the king sent for the hunter.

"Well, hunter," he said, "what is new in the jungle?" And the hunter told him:

"Sire, a bull and a lion who are fast friends. They even share the same cave."

"That must be a fine thing to see," said the king. "I must come one day, to see them."

In time, a jackal went to live with the lion and the bull. When the lion made a kill, he let the jackal eat what he left. The jackal now ate so well that he grew fat. And as he grew fat, he grew proud.

"All I have to eat is what the lion has left," he said. "I will make the bull and the lion fight. The bull will kill the lion; and the lion will kill the bull. And I shall have both lion and bull to eat."

So the jackal went to the bull, and said to him:

"My lord, the lion is no true friend to you. When you are not here, he sneers at your hoofs and horns."

"Is that so?" cried the bull. And he saw red.

Then the jackal went to the lion, and said to him:

"My lord, the bull is no true friend to you. When you are not here, he sneers at your paws and mane."

"Is that so?" cried the lion. And he swung his tail in rage.

And as soon as they met, they began to fight.

That same day, the king sent for the hunter.

"Well, hunter," he said, "how are your jungle friends, the bull and the lion?"

And the hunter told him, "Oh, Sire, they have a jackal with them now."

"A jackal?" cried the king. "That is bad. A jackal will harm them if he can. Come, hunter; take me to them at once."

So the hunter led the king to the cave in the jungle. They got to it just as the bull and the lion had begun to fight.

"Stop!" cried the king.

The bull and the lion saw it was the king who spoke. At once they drew back, and stood still.

The king went on: "Why do two such fast friends fight?"

"Sire," said the bull, "the lion sneers at my hoofs and horns."

"Sire," said the lion, "the bull sneers at my paws and mane."

"But, Lion, that is not true!" cried the bull.

"But, Bull, that is not true!" cried the lion.

"What told you this?" asked the king.

"Sire, the jackal told me," said the bull.

"Sire, the jackal told me," said the lion.

"Sire, I did not," said the jackal.

"Sire, he lies!" cried the bull.

"Sire, he lies!" cried the lion.

"If he lies now," said the king, "can you not see that he also lied then?"

"Jackal, come here!" cried the bull. "This hoof you

spoke of is hard. With it I shall whack you till you wail."

"Jackal, come here!" cried the lion. "This paw you spoke of is strong. With it I shall pull your right ear till you yell."

But the jackal slunk off. And they never saw him again from that day.

"Do not fall prey to a mean mind again," said the king. "Stay good friends as long as you live."

"Sire, we will not," said the bull.

"Sire, we will," said the lion.

And they did not. And they did.

The Hare in the Moon

SASA THE HARE had his lair in a wood. He was a gentle hare, with fur like silk.

In this wood grew a mango tree. In this mango tree a monkey had his lair.

This wood stood on a hill. On this hill a jackal had his lair.

At the foot of this hill ran a river. By this river an otter had his lair.

The otter, the jackal, the monkey, and Sasa the hare were fast friends.

One day, at dusk, they all four met. They saw the moon grow bright in the sky. They saw that it was a full moon.

Then said Sasa the hare, "The day after full moon is

a day to give gifts. If a beggar needs food on that day, we must feed him with our own food."

"So we will," said the other three.

At dawn next day, a man got up, and went to the river to fish. He got seven red fish on his line. He hid them in the sand on the river bank, and went on up the river, to try to catch more.

At dawn, too, the otter had left his lair to look for food. He smelled a fish smell in the sand, and dug. He dug up the seven red fish.

The otter cried out three times:

"Who owns seven red fish?"

"Who owns seven red fish?"

"Who owns seven red fish?"

No one said, "I do."

So the otter took the seven red fish to his lair.

At dawn the jackal left his lair to look for food. He went to the hut of the man who had gone to fish.

In it he saw a pot of milk. No one was in the hut with it.

The jackal cried out three times:

"Who owns a pot of milk?"

"Who owns a pot of milk?"

"Who owns a pot of milk?"

No one said, "I do."

So the jackal put his head into the cord of the milk pot and took it to his lair.

At dawn the monkey left his lair to look for food. He saw a big mango on his mango tree.

113

The monkey cried out three times:
"Who owns this mango?"
"Who owns this mango?"
"Who owns this mango?"
No one said, "I do."

So the monkey put the mango on his shelf. His shelf was a fork in the mango tree, just by his lair.

At dawn Sasa the hare left his lair to look for food. "I will eat grass," he said. But then he added:

"This is the day after full moon. This is a day to give gifts. If a beggar asks me for food today, I must give him my own food. But man needs more than grass. So I must give him my own self!"

2

NOW THE KING of the Sky sat up in the air, and the air he sat on grew hot when Sasa the hare said this. So the King of the Sky went down to the wood to find out why. He put on the rags of a beggar, and he took a clay bowl in his hand. He went first to the lair of the otter.

He said to the otter, "Sir Otter, I need food."

"Good," said the otter. "I will give you food. I will give you my seven red fish."

And out he came with the seven red fish laid on a fresh green palm leaf.

"Thank you," said the beggar, and he put the seven red fish in his bowl.

Then he went to the lair of the jackal.

He said to the jackal, "Sir Jackal, I need food."

"Good," said the jackal. "I will give you food. I will give you my pot of milk."

And out he came with the milk pot slung from his neck.

"Thank you," said the beggar, and he put the milk into his bowl.

115

Then he went to the lair of the monkey.

He said to the monkey, "Sir Monkey, I need food."

"Good," said the monkey. "I will give you food. I will give you my big mango."

And down he sprang with the mango from his tall mango shelf.

"Thank you," said the beggar, and he put the mango into his bowl.

Then he went to the lair of Sasa the hare.

He said to Sasa the hare:

"Sir Sasa, I need food."

"Good," said Sasa the hare. "I will give you food. I will give you my own self. Make a fire, Sir Beggar, and I will jump into it."

So the beggar lit a fire. Sasa the hare stood by the fire.

"Small beasts that live in my fur," he said, "you must not die with me."

And three times he shook the fur that was like silk, to shake the small beasts off, to keep them safe.

Then he sprang into the fire. But the fire was as cold as ice.

"How is this, Sir Beggar?" cried Sasa the hare. "The fire is as cold as ice!"

Then the beggar told him:

"Sasa, I am the King of the Sky. As long as the moon lasts, men shall see you in it when it is full, to keep them in mind of the kind deed you did today."

Then the King of the Sky took Sasa the hare out of

116

the cold fire and put him down to rest on the soft grass. He took clay from the hill; and with the clay he drew Sasa the hare on the disc of the full moon.

And that is why, when the moon is full, we can still see Sasa the hare in it, to keep us in mind of this tale.